Cling Journal

Drawing Closer to God as a Lifestyle

Kim Cash Tate

Drawing Closer to God JOURNAL as a Lifestyle

Cover design and interior layout: Spechouse Creative
Tate, Kimberly Cash.
Cling Journal – Drawing Closer to God as a Lifestyle / Kim Cash Tate.
ISBN: 978-1-946336-04-0

ALSO BY KIM CASH TATE

Heavenly Places
Faithful
Cherished
Hope Springs
The Color of Hope
Hidden Blessings
Though I Stumble
If I Believe
If You're With Me
When I'm Tempted

Cling: Choosing a Lifestyle of Intimacy with God

From my heart to yours ~

Please know as you open this journal that I have prayed for you. It is my prayer that the Lord meets you in an intimate way in these pages. I pray He uses it to draw you closer to Himself and to cultivate a deeper relationship—a lifestyle of walking closely with Him.

I don't write as one who has "arrived". I am desperate myself to daily cling to God. From a study of Deuteronomy eighteen years ago, when that word "cling" first grabbed me, my heart's cry has been, "Lord, help me to cling to You." I have seen His faithfulness in answering that prayer, in revealing Himself through His word, and in drawing me close day-to-day—season-to-season—simply as I look to Him, talk to Him, and hear from Him.

I encourage you to talk to the Lord in an intimate way in this journal. Day by day, share your joys, frustrations, heartaches, and praises. Be real about your doubts and fears, the nagging worries, and the secret longings. Allow Him to be your refuge, your go-to, your closest Friend.

The invitation comes straight from above—cling to Him.

In Christ,

Kim

"You shall follow the LORD your

God and fear Him;

and you shall keep His

commandments, listen to

His voice, serve Him,

and cling to Him."

(Deuteronomy 13:4)

*What opportunities to cling to God did
life present today?*

How specifically did you cling in those situations?

*How did you cling to God as a lifestyle today—through His
word, prayer, praise, and/or thanks?*

*Cling to God right now by writing your thoughts
directly to Him in this journal.*

Drawing Closer to God **cling** *as a Lifestyle*
JOURNAL

*What opportunities to cling to God did
life present today?*

How specifically did you cling in those situations?

*How did you cling to God as a lifestyle today—through His
word, prayer, praise, and/or thanks?*

*Cling to God right now by writing your thoughts
directly to Him in this journal.*

*What opportunities to cling to God did
life present today?*

How specifically did you cling in those situations?

*How did you cling to God as a lifestyle today—through His
word, prayer, praise, and/or thanks?*

*Cling to God right now by writing your thoughts
directly to Him in this journal.*

What opportunities to cling to God did
life present today?

How specifically did you cling in those situations?

How did you cling to God as a lifestyle today—through His
word, prayer, praise, and/or thanks?

Cling to God right now by writing your thoughts
directly to Him in this journal.

"*You shall follow the LORD your*

God and fear Him;

and you shall keep His

commandments, listen to

His voice, serve Him,

and cling to Him."

(Deuteronomy 13:4)

*What opportunities to cling to God did
life present today?*

How specifically did you cling in those situations?

*How did you cling to God as a lifestyle today—through His
word, prayer, praise, and/or thanks?*

*Cling to God right now by writing your thoughts
directly to Him in this journal.*

What opportunities to cling to God did life present today?

How specifically did you cling in those situations?

How did you cling to God as a lifestyle today—through His word, prayer, praise, and/or thanks?

Cling to God right now by writing your thoughts directly to Him in this journal.

*What opportunities to cling to God did
life present today?*

How specifically did you cling in those situations?

*How did you cling to God as a lifestyle today—through His
word, prayer, praise, and/or thanks?*

*Cling to God right now by writing your thoughts
directly to Him in this journal.*

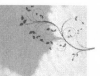

What opportunities to cling to God did life present today?

How specifically did you cling in those situations?

How did you cling to God as a lifestyle today—through His word, prayer, praise, and/or thanks?

Cling to God right now by writing your thoughts directly to Him in this journal.

"I am the vine,

you are the branches;

he who abides in Me and I in him,

he bears much fruit,

for apart from Me

you can do nothing."

(John 15:5)

*What opportunities to cling to God did
life present today?*

How specifically did you cling in those situations?

*How did you cling to God as a lifestyle today—through His
word, prayer, praise, and/or thanks?*

*Cling to God right now by writing your thoughts
directly to Him in this journal.*

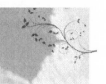

*What opportunities to cling to God did
life present today?*

How specifically did you cling in those situations?

*How did you cling to God as a lifestyle today—through His
word, prayer, praise, and/or thanks?*

*Cling to God right now by writing your thoughts
directly to Him in this journal.*

*What opportunities to cling to God did
life present today?*

How specifically did you cling in those situations?

*How did you cling to God as a lifestyle today—through His
word, prayer, praise, and/or thanks?*

*Cling to God right now by writing your thoughts
directly to Him in this journal.*

Drawing Closer to God *cling* JOURNAL as a Lifestyle

What opportunities to cling to God did life present today?

How specifically did you cling in those situations?

How did you cling to God as a lifestyle today—through His word, prayer, praise, and/or thanks?

Cling to God right now by writing your thoughts directly to Him in this journal.

" . . . I am with you always,

even to the end of the age."

(Matthew 28:20)

*What opportunities to cling to God did
life present today?*

How specifically did you cling in those situations?

*How did you cling to God as a lifestyle today—through His
word, prayer, praise, and/or thanks?*

*Cling to God right now by writing your thoughts
directly to Him in this journal.*

*What opportunities to cling to God did
life present today?*

How specifically did you cling in those situations?

*How did you cling to God as a lifestyle today—through His
word, prayer, praise, and/or thanks?*

*Cling to God right now by writing your thoughts
directly to Him in this journal.*

*What opportunities to cling to God did
life present today?*

How specifically did you cling in those situations?

*How did you cling to God as a lifestyle today—through His
word, prayer, praise, and/or thanks?*

*Cling to God right now by writing your thoughts
directly to Him in this journal.*

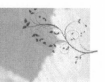

*What opportunities to cling to God did
life present today?*

How specifically did you cling in those situations?

*How did you cling to God as a lifestyle today—through His
word, prayer, praise, and/or thanks?*

*Cling to God right now by writing your thoughts
directly to Him in this journal.*

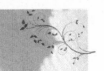

"My soul clings to You;

Your right hand upholds me."

(Psalm 63:8)

*What opportunities to cling to God did
life present today?*

How specifically did you cling in those situations?

*How did you cling to God as a lifestyle today—through His
word, prayer, praise, and/or thanks?*

*Cling to God right now by writing your thoughts
directly to Him in this journal.*

Drawing Closer to God **cling** *as a Lifestyle*
JOURNAL

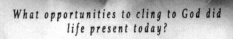

What opportunities to cling to God did
life present today?

How specifically did you cling in those situations?

How did you cling to God as a lifestyle today—through His
word, prayer, praise, and/or thanks?

Cling to God right now by writing your thoughts
directly to Him in this journal.

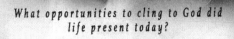

*What opportunities to cling to God did
life present today?*

How specifically did you cling in those situations?

*How did you cling to God as a lifestyle today—through His
word, prayer, praise, and/or thanks?*

*Cling to God right now by writing your thoughts
directly to Him in this journal.*

What opportunities to cling to God did
life present today?

How specifically did you cling in those situations?

How did you cling to God as a lifestyle today—through His
word, prayer, praise, and/or thanks?

Cling to God right now by writing your thoughts
directly to Him in this journal.

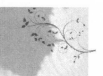

"But you are to cling to the

LORD your God, as you have

done to this day."

(Joshua 23:8)

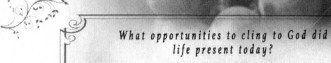

*What opportunities to cling to God did
life present today?*

How specifically did you cling in those situations?

*How did you cling to God as a lifestyle today—through His
word, prayer, praise, and/or thanks?*

*Cling to God right now by writing your thoughts
directly to Him in this journal.*

*What opportunities to cling to God did
life present today?*

How specifically did you cling in those situations?

*How did you cling to God as a lifestyle today—through His
word, prayer, praise, and/or thanks?*

*Cling to God right now by writing your thoughts
directly to Him in this journal.*

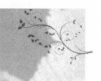

*What opportunities to cling to God did
life present today?*

How specifically did you cling in those situations?

*How did you cling to God as a lifestyle today—through His
word, prayer, praise, and/or thanks?*

*Cling to God right now by writing your thoughts
directly to Him in this journal.*

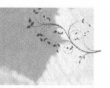

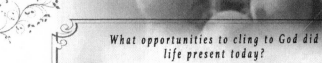

*What opportunities to cling to God did
life present today?*

How specifically did you cling in those situations?

*How did you cling to God as a lifestyle today—through His
word, prayer, praise, and/or thanks?*

*Cling to God right now by writing your thoughts
directly to Him in this journal.*

Drawing Closer to God **cling** as a Lifestyle
JOURNAL

"*Draw near to God*

and He will

draw near to you."

(James 4:8)

*What opportunities to cling to God did
life present today?*

How specifically did you cling in those situations?

*How did you cling to God as a lifestyle today—through His
word, prayer, praise, and/or thanks?*

*Cling to God right now by writing your thoughts
directly to Him in this journal.*

*What opportunities to cling to God did
life present today?*

How specifically did you cling in those situations?

*How did you cling to God as a lifestyle today—through His
word, prayer, praise, and/or thanks?*

*Cling to God right now by writing your thoughts
directly to Him in this journal.*

Drawing Closer to God *cling* as a Lifestyle
JOURNAL

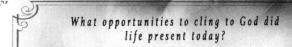

What opportunities to cling to God did
life present today?

How specifically did you cling in those situations?

How did you cling to God as a lifestyle today—through His
word, prayer, praise, and/or thanks?

Cling to God right now by writing your thoughts
directly to Him in this journal.

What opportunities to cling to God did
life present today?

How specifically did you cling in those situations?

How did you cling to God as a lifestyle today—through His
word, prayer, praise, and/or thanks?

Cling to God right now by writing your thoughts
directly to Him in this journal.

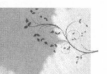

Drawing Closer to God **cling** *as a Lifestyle*
JOURNAL

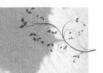

Drawing Closer to God **cling** as a Lifestyle
JOURNAL

"He who dwells in the

shelter of the Most High

Will abide in the shadow

of the Almighty."

(Psalm 91:1)

What opportunities to cling to God did
life present today?

How specifically did you cling in those situations?

How did you cling to God as a lifestyle today—through His
word, prayer, praise, and/or thanks?

Cling to God right now by writing your thoughts
directly to Him in this journal.

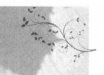

Drawing Closer to God **cling** *as a Lifestyle*
JOURNAL

*What opportunities to cling to God did
life present today?*

How specifically did you cling in those situations?

*How did you cling to God as a lifestyle today—through His
word, prayer, praise, and/or thanks?*

*Cling to God right now by writing your thoughts
directly to Him in this journal.*

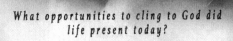

*What opportunities to cling to God did
life present today?*

How specifically did you cling in those situations?

*How did you cling to God as a lifestyle today—through His
word, prayer, praise, and/or thanks?*

*Cling to God right now by writing your thoughts
directly to Him in this journal.*

_____

_____

_____

_____

_____

_____

_____

_____

_____

_____

_____

_____

_____

_____

_____

*What opportunities to cling to God did
life present today?*

How specifically did you cling in those situations?

*How did you cling to God as a lifestyle today—through His
word, prayer, praise, and/or thanks?*

*Cling to God right now by writing your thoughts
directly to Him in this journal.*

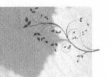

Drawing Closer to God **cling** _as a Lifestyle_
JOURNAL

"But as for me,

the nearness of God

is my good . . ."

(Psalm 73:28)

What opportunities to cling to God did life present today?

How specifically did you cling in those situations?

How did you cling to God as a lifestyle today—through His word, prayer, praise, and/or thanks?

Cling to God right now by writing your thoughts directly to Him in this journal.

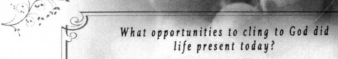

*What opportunities to cling to God did
life present today?*

How specifically did you cling in those situations?

*How did you cling to God as a lifestyle today—through His
word, prayer, praise, and/or thanks?*

*Cling to God right now by writing your thoughts
directly to Him in this journal.*

*What opportunities to cling to God did
life present today?*

How specifically did you cling in those situations?

*How did you cling to God as a lifestyle today—through His
word, prayer, praise, and/or thanks?*

*Cling to God right now by writing your thoughts
directly to Him in this journal.*

*What opportunities to cling to God did
life present today?*

How specifically did you cling in those situations?

*How did you cling to God as a lifestyle today—through His
word, prayer, praise, and/or thanks?*

*Cling to God right now by writing your thoughts
directly to Him in this journal.*

Drawing Closer to God cling as a Lifestyle
JOURNAL

Drawing Closer to God **cling** JOURNAL *as a Lifestyle*

"Be gracious to me, O God,

be gracious to me,

For my soul takes refuge in You;

And in the shadow of Your wings

I will take refuge . . ."

(Psalm 57:1)

What opportunities to cling to God did
life present today?

How specifically did you cling in those situations?

How did you cling to God as a lifestyle today—through His
word, prayer, praise, and/or thanks?

Cling to God right now by writing your thoughts
directly to Him in this journal.

*What opportunities to cling to God did
life present today?*

How specifically did you cling in those situations?

*How did you cling to God as a lifestyle today—through His
word, prayer, praise, and/or thanks?*

*Cling to God right now by writing your thoughts
directly to Him in this journal.*

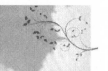

Drawing Closer to God *cling* as a Lifestyle
JOURNAL

*What opportunities to cling to God did
life present today?*

How specifically did you cling in those situations?

*How did you cling to God as a lifestyle today—through His
word, prayer, praise, and/or thanks?*

*Cling to God right now by writing your thoughts
directly to Him in this journal.*

Drawing Closer to God **cling** *as a Lifestyle*
JOURNAL

*What opportunities to cling to God did
life present today?*

How specifically did you cling in those situations?

*How did you cling to God as a lifestyle today—through His
word, prayer, praise, and/or thanks?*

*Cling to God right now by writing your thoughts
directly to Him in this journal.*

"'I love You, O LORD, my strength.'

The LORD is my rock

and my fortress and my deliverer,

My God, my rock,

in whom I take refuge;

My shield and the horn of my

salvation, my stronghold.

I call upon the LORD,

who is worthy to be praised,

And I am saved from my enemies."

(Psalm 18:1-3)

What opportunities to cling to God did
life present today?

How specifically did you cling in those situations?

How did you cling to God as a lifestyle today—through His
word, prayer, praise, and/or thanks?

Cling to God right now by writing your thoughts
directly to Him in this journal.

*What opportunities to cling to God did
life present today?*

How specifically did you cling in those situations?

*How did you cling to God as a lifestyle today—through His
word, prayer, praise, and/or thanks?*

*Cling to God right now by writing your thoughts
directly to Him in this journal.*

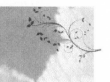

What opportunities to cling to God did
life present today?

How specifically did you cling in those situations?

How did you cling to God as a lifestyle today—through His
word, prayer, praise, and/or thanks?

Cling to God right now by writing your thoughts
directly to Him in this journal.

*What opportunities to cling to God did
life present today?*

How specifically did you cling in those situations?

*How did you cling to God as a lifestyle today—through His
word, prayer, praise, and/or thanks?*

*Cling to God right now by writing your thoughts
directly to Him in this journal.*

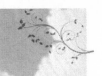

"Rejoice always;

pray without ceasing;

in everything give thanks;

for this is God's will for you

in Christ Jesus."

(1 Thessalonians 5:16-18)

*What opportunities to cling to God did
life present today?*

How specifically did you cling in those situations?

*How did you cling to God as a lifestyle today—through His
word, prayer, praise, and/or thanks?*

*Cling to God right now by writing your thoughts
directly to Him in this journal.*

*What opportunities to cling to God did
life present today?*

How specifically did you cling in those situations?

*How did you cling to God as a lifestyle today—through His
word, prayer, praise, and/or thanks?*

*Cling to God right now by writing your thoughts
directly to Him in this journal.*

*What opportunities to cling to God did
life present today?*

How specifically did you cling in those situations?

*How did you cling to God as a lifestyle today—through His
word, prayer, praise, and/or thanks?*

*Cling to God right now by writing your thoughts
directly to Him in this journal.*

*What opportunities to cling to God did
life present today?*

How specifically did you cling in those situations?

*How did you cling to God as a lifestyle today—through His
word, prayer, praise, and/or thanks?*

*Cling to God right now by writing your thoughts
directly to Him in this journal.*

Drawing Closer to God **cling** as a Lifestyle
JOURNAL

"You shall fear the LORD your

God; you shall serve Him and

cling to Him, and you shall

swear by His name."

(Deuteronomy 10:20)

What opportunities to cling to God did life present today?

How specifically did you cling in those situations?

How did you cling to God as a lifestyle today—through His word, prayer, praise, and/or thanks?

Cling to God right now by writing your thoughts directly to Him in this journal.

What opportunities to cling to God did
life present today?

How specifically did you cling in those situations?

How did you cling to God as a lifestyle today—through His
word, prayer, praise, and/or thanks?

Cling to God right now by writing your thoughts
directly to Him in this journal.

What opportunities to cling to God did
life present today?

How specifically did you cling in those situations?

How did you cling to God as a lifestyle today—through His
word, prayer, praise, and/or thanks?

Cling to God right now by writing your thoughts
directly to Him in this journal.

What opportunities to cling to God did
life present today?

How specifically did you cling in those situations?

How did you cling to God as a lifestyle today—through His
word, prayer, praise, and/or thanks?

Cling to God right now by writing your thoughts
directly to Him in this journal.

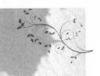

Drawing Closer to God **cling** *as a Lifestyle*
JOURNAL

"*You shall love the LORD your*

God with all your heart and

with all your soul

and with all your might."

(Deuteronomy 6:5)

*What opportunities to cling to God did
life present today?*

How specifically did you cling in those situations?

*How did you cling to God as a lifestyle today—through His
word, prayer, praise, and/or thanks?*

*Cling to God right now by writing your thoughts
directly to Him in this journal.*

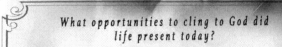

*What opportunities to cling to God did
life present today?*

How specifically did you cling in those situations?

*How did you cling to God as a lifestyle today—through His
word, prayer, praise, and/or thanks?*

*Cling to God right now by writing your thoughts
directly to Him in this journal.*

What opportunities to cling to God did life present today?

How specifically did you cling in those situations?

How did you cling to God as a lifestyle today—through His word, prayer, praise, and/or thanks?

Cling to God right now by writing your thoughts directly to Him in this journal.

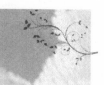

*What opportunities to cling to God did
life present today?*

How specifically did you cling in those situations?

*How did you cling to God as a lifestyle today—through His
word, prayer, praise, and/or thanks?*

**Cling to God right now by writing your thoughts
directly to Him in this journal.**

 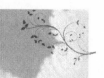

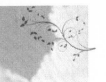

Drawing Closer to God **cling** *as a Lifestyle*
JOURNAL

"We love,

because He first loved us."

(1 John 4:19)

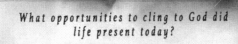

What opportunities to cling to God did
life present today?

How specifically did you cling in those situations?

How did you cling to God as a lifestyle today—through His
word, prayer, praise, and/or thanks?

Cling to God right now by writing your thoughts
directly to Him in this journal.

What opportunities to cling to God did
life present today?

How specifically did you cling in those situations?

How did you cling to God as a lifestyle today—through His
word, prayer, praise, and/or thanks?

Cling to God right now by writing your thoughts
directly to Him in this journal.

What opportunities to cling to God did life present today?

How specifically did you cling in those situations?

How did you cling to God as a lifestyle today—through His word, prayer, praise, and/or thanks?

Cling to God right now by writing your thoughts directly to Him in this journal.

*What opportunities to cling to God did
life present today?*

How specifically did you cling in those situations?

*How did you cling to God as a lifestyle today—through His
word, prayer, praise, and/or thanks?*

*Cling to God right now by writing your thoughts
directly to Him in this journal.*

"*For You have been my help,*

And in the shadow of Your

wings I sing for joy."

(Psalm 63:7)

*What opportunities to cling to God did
life present today?*

How specifically did you cling in those situations?

*How did you cling to God as a lifestyle today—through His
word, prayer, praise, and/or thanks?*

*Cling to God right now by writing your thoughts
directly to Him in this journal.*

*What opportunities to cling to God did
life present today?*

How specifically did you cling in those situations?

*How did you cling to God as a lifestyle today—through His
word, prayer, praise, and/or thanks?*

*Cling to God right now by writing your thoughts
directly to Him in this journal.*

*What opportunities to cling to God did
life present today?*

How specifically did you cling in those situations?

*How did you cling to God as a lifestyle today—through His
word, prayer, praise, and/or thanks?*

*Cling to God right now by writing your thoughts
directly to Him in this journal.*

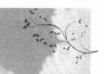

*What opportunities to cling to God did
life present today?*

How specifically did you cling in those situations?

*How did you cling to God as a lifestyle today—through His
word, prayer, praise, and/or thanks?*

*Cling to God right now by writing your thoughts
directly to Him in this journal.*

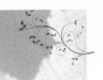

"Delight yourself in the LORD;

And He will give you the

desires of your heart.

Commit your way to the LORD,

Trust also in Him,

and He will do it."

(Psalm 37:4-5)

What opportunities to cling to God did
life present today?

How specifically did you cling in those situations?

How did you cling to God as a lifestyle today—through His
word, prayer, praise, and/or thanks?

Cling to God right now by writing your thoughts
directly to Him in this journal.

What opportunities to cling to God did life present today?

How specifically did you cling in those situations?

How did you cling to God as a lifestyle today—through His word, prayer, praise, and/or thanks?

Cling to God right now by writing your thoughts directly to Him in this journal.

*What opportunities to cling to God did
life present today?*

How specifically did you cling in those situations?

*How did you cling to God as a lifestyle today—through His
word, prayer, praise, and/or thanks?*

*Cling to God right now by writing your thoughts
directly to Him in this journal.*

*What opportunities to cling to God did
life present today?*

How specifically did you cling in those situations?

*How did you cling to God as a lifestyle today—through His
word, prayer, praise, and/or thanks?*

*Cling to God right now by writing your thoughts
directly to Him in this journal.*

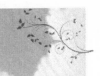

"... I have poured out my

soul before the LORD."

(1 Samuel 1:15)

*What opportunities to cling to God did
life present today?*

How specifically did you cling in those situations?

*How did you cling to God as a lifestyle today—through His
word, prayer, praise, and/or thanks?*

*Cling to God right now by writing your thoughts
directly to Him in this journal.*

*What opportunities to cling to God did
life present today?*

How specifically did you cling in those situations?

*How did you cling to God as a lifestyle today—through His
word, prayer, praise, and/or thanks?*

*Cling to God right now by writing your thoughts
directly to Him in this journal.*

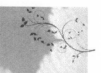

Drawing Closer to God **cling** *as a Lifestyle*
JOURNAL

What opportunities to cling to God did
life present today?

How specifically did you cling in those situations?

How did you cling to God as a lifestyle today—through His
word, prayer, praise, and/or thanks?

Cling to God right now by writing your thoughts
directly to Him in this journal.

*What opportunities to cling to God did
life present today?*

How specifically did you cling in those situations?

*How did you cling to God as a lifestyle today—through His
word, prayer, praise, and/or thanks?*

*Cling to God right now by writing your thoughts
directly to Him in this journal.*

"Seek the LORD

and His strength;

Seek His face continually."

(Psalm 105:4)

*What opportunities to cling to God did
life present today?*

How specifically did you cling in those situations?

*How did you cling to God as a lifestyle today—through His
word, prayer, praise, and/or thanks?*

*Cling to God right now by writing your thoughts
directly to Him in this journal.*

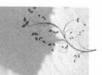

Drawing Closer to God **cling** as a Lifestyle
JOURNAL

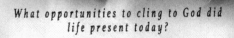

*What opportunities to cling to God did
life present today?*

How specifically did you cling in those situations?

*How did you cling to God as a lifestyle today—through His
word, prayer, praise, and/or thanks?*

*Cling to God right now by writing your thoughts
directly to Him in this journal.*

What opportunities to cling to God did
life present today?

How specifically did you cling in those situations?

How did you cling to God as a lifestyle today—through His
word, prayer, praise, and/or thanks?

Cling to God right now by writing your thoughts
directly to Him in this journal.

*What opportunities to cling to God did
life present today?*

How specifically did you cling in those situations?

*How did you cling to God as a lifestyle today—through His
word, prayer, praise, and/or thanks?*

*Cling to God right now by writing your thoughts
directly to Him in this journal.*

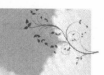

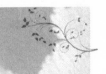

"*My sheep hear My voice,*

and I know them,

and they follow Me;

and I give eternal life to them,

and they will never perish;

and no one will snatch them

out of My hand."

(John 10:27-29)

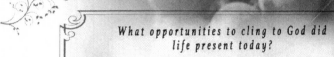

*What opportunities to cling to God did
life present today?*

How specifically did you cling in those situations?

*How did you cling to God as a lifestyle today—through His
word, prayer, praise, and/or thanks?*

*Cling to God right now by writing your thoughts
directly to Him in this journal.*

*What opportunities to cling to God did
life present today?*

How specifically did you cling in those situations?

*How did you cling to God as a lifestyle today—through His
word, prayer, praise, and/or thanks?*

*Cling to God right now by writing your thoughts
directly to Him in this journal.*

What opportunities to cling to God did
life present today?

How specifically did you cling in those situations?

How did you cling to God as a lifestyle today—through His
word, prayer, praise, and/or thanks?

Cling to God right now by writing your thoughts
directly to Him in this journal.

Drawing Closer to God **cling** as a Lifestyle
JOURNAL

*What opportunities to cling to God did
life present today?*

How specifically did you cling in those situations?

*How did you cling to God as a lifestyle today—through His
word, prayer, praise, and/or thanks?*

*Cling to God right now by writing your thoughts
directly to Him in this journal.*

Drawing Closer to God **cling** *as a Lifestyle*
JOURNAL

"Abhor what is evil;

cling to what is good."

(Romans 12:9)

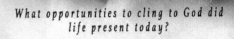

What opportunities to cling to God did
life present today?

How specifically did you cling in those situations?

How did you cling to God as a lifestyle today—through His
word, prayer, praise, and/or thanks?

Cling to God right now by writing your thoughts
directly to Him in this journal.

Drawing Closer to God **cling** *as a Lifestyle*
JOURNAL

What opportunities to cling to God did
life present today?

How specifically did you cling in those situations?

How did you cling to God as a lifestyle today—through His
word, prayer, praise, and/or thanks?

Cling to God right now by writing your thoughts
directly to Him in this journal.

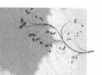

*What opportunities to cling to God did
life present today?*

How specifically did you cling in those situations?

*How did you cling to God as a lifestyle today—through His
word, prayer, praise, and/or thanks?*

*Cling to God right now by writing your thoughts
directly to Him in this journal.*

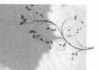

Drawing Closer to God **cling** *as a Lifestyle*

JOURNAL

*What opportunities to cling to God did
life present today?*

How specifically did you cling in those situations?

*How did you cling to God as a lifestyle today—through His
word, prayer, praise, and/or thanks?*

*Cling to God right now by writing your thoughts
directly to Him in this journal.*

Drawing Closer to God **cling** *as a Lifestyle*
JOURNAL

Made in the USA
Middletown, DE
10 December 2019